What Color Is Your Day?

Written by Camryn Wells
Illustrated by Eleanor Loseby

First paperback edition September 2019

Book design by Eleanor Loseby

ISBN 978-1-989123-09-6
www.camrynwells.com

To my children, Monroe and Yuna.
Whatever you feel is beautiful
because it is you.

What color is your day, my love?
Is it blue, is it green or gray?

Explore the shades and hues you feel
When you laugh or cry or play.

Are you blue like a
wilted flower
That's waiting
for the sun?

Or does blue just make
you calmly reflect
On everything
you've done?

Pink fills your heart with kindness,
And tickles you with joy.
You might feel pink when you're silly
Or playing with your toys.

Which brings us on to purple,
A friendly hue of blue.
Original and individual
Are purple's traits of you.

Orange and yellow are best of buds,
They play so well together.

They're creative, social butterflies,
Like a play date in sunny weather.

Green can feel like envy,
When you want what isn't yours.

But green can also feel quite fresh,
When your happiness is restored.

Red is a youthful color,
It's exciting and bold, too!
It is powerful and loving,

A true reflection of you.

And don't forget the color brown
When you're feeling safe and sound.
It is beautiful and earthy,
Like tree roots in the ground.

Sometimes feelings can be complex,
They're not always black or white.

You might feel more like a moody gray,
And that's perfectly alright.

So what color is your day, my love?
Or maybe you feel more than one.

Ask yourself at the start of each day
And again when the day is done.

Are you feeling green or maybe orange?
Black or red or blue?

Or maybe yellow AND some pink
And a splash of purple, too!

The colors that describe your day,
Can change with how you feel.

Happy, embarrassed, confused or mad,
These emotions are all quite real.

But more importantly, they are yours,

So feel as long as you may.

For a moment in time or a few hours more,

Or one color for the day.

And when you're ready, the choice is yours,
To feel a new color or hue.

Whatever you choose, whatever you feel
Is beautiful because it is you.

Dear Young Reader,

I hope that you enjoyed reading about different colors and emotions that you might feel every day. Here's a fun little secret for you...adults feel a lot of colorful emotions, too!

Understanding your emotions is the first step to managing them. And managing them can help you build positive attitudes and behaviors. So, the next time you don't know how you feel, take a deep breath...aaahhh...and read this book to help you figure it out.

You might also enjoy listening to me read this story as a video book! If so, please ask an adult to sign up at camrynwells.com/video.

Finally, a great big THANK YOU for reading this book! I sincerely hope you enjoyed it because I loved writing it for young readers like you!

Kindest regards,
Camryn Wells

When she isn't playing with words, Camryn and her husband, Adam, are busy raising their two young children. Monroe is her tenacious three-year-old son and the inspiration behind What Color is Your Day?. Her daughter, Yuna, is one-year-old and - fun fact - shares a birthday with Camryn!

Eleanor Loseby is an illustrator and animator from England, UK. She loves making art that makes someone smile, through digital or traditional (and messy!) methods. When she isn't creating, dropping her paintbrush in her tea, or coming up with bonkers animation ideas, Eleanor loves to practice yoga and drive to new and exciting places that she can draw.

Made in the USA
Monee, IL
15 January 2020